Based on the best-selling keyboard method *by Kenneth Baker.*

THE COMPLE
KEYBOARD PLA

Classic Hits

This publication is not authorised for sale in
the United States of America and/or Canada

Wise Publications
part of The Music Sales Group
London/New York/Paris/Sydney/Copenhagen/Berlin/Madrid/Tokyo

Published by
Wise Publications
14-15 Berners Street, London W1T 3LJ, UK.

Exclusive Distributors:
Music Sales Limited
Distribution Centre, Newmarket Road,
Bury St Edmunds, Suffolk IP33 3YB, UK.
Music Sales Pty Limited
120 Rothschild Avenue, Rosebery, NSW 2018, Australia.

This book © Copyright 2006 Wise Publications,
a division of Music Sales Limited.
Order No. AM986293
ISBN 1-84609-652-9

Compiled by Nick Crispin.
Music arranged by Paul Honey.
Music processed by Paul Ewers Music Design.
Cover photograph courtesy of London Features International.
Printed in the EU.

Your Guarantee of Quality
As publishers, we strive to produce every book
to the highest commercial standards.
This book has been carefully designed to minimise awkward
page turns and to make playing from it a real pleasure.
Particular care has been given to specifying acid-free, neutral-sized paper
made from pulps which have not been elemental chlorine bleached.
This pulp is from farmed sustainable forests and was produced with special
regard for the environment. Throughout, the printing and binding have been
planned to ensure a sturdy, attractive publication which should give years of enjoyment.
If your copy fails to meet our high standards, please inform us and
we will gladly replace it.

www.musicsales.com

Angie

Words & Music by Mick Jagger & Keith Richards

Voice: **Flute**
Rhythm: **Soft rock**
Tempo: ♩ = 72

Oh An - gie, __ oh An - gie, when will those dark clouds dis - ap-

-pear? _____ An - gie, __ An - gie, __

where will it lead us from here? _____ With no

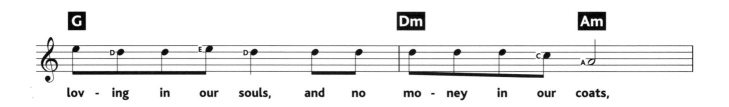

lov - ing in our souls, and no mo - ney in our coats,

you can't say we're sat - is - fied. _____ But

An - gie, ___ An - gie, you can't say we've nev - er

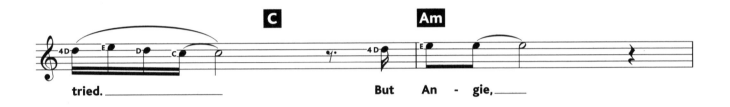

tried. _____ But An - gie, _____

An - - gie, ain't it good to be a -

-live? _____ An - gie, ___ An - gie,

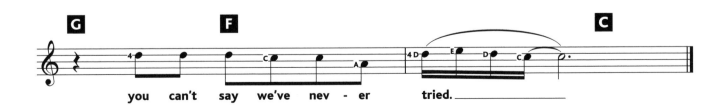

you can't say we've nev - er tried. _____

Brothers In Arms

Words & Music by Mark Knopfler

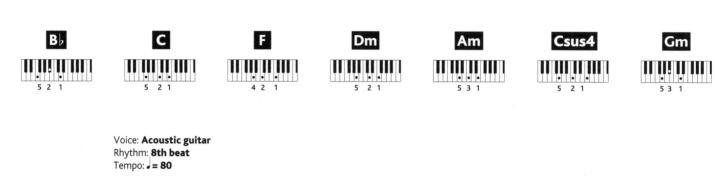

Voice: **Acoustic guitar**
Rhythm: **8th beat**
Tempo: ♩ = 80

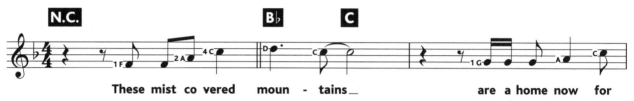

These mist co vered moun - tains __ are a home now for

me, but my home is the low - lands, __

and al - ways will be. Some day you'll re - turn __

__ to __ your val - leys and your farms,

new hand position

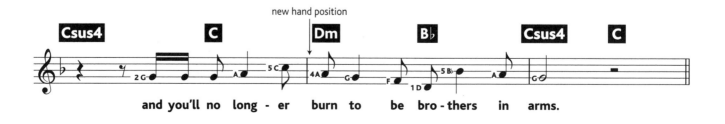

and you'll no long - er burn to be bro - thers in arms.

Through these fields of des-

- truc - tion, ___ bap - ti - sms of fire, ___

I've watched all your suf - fer - ing ___ as the bat -tles raged

higher. And though they did hurt me so bad ___

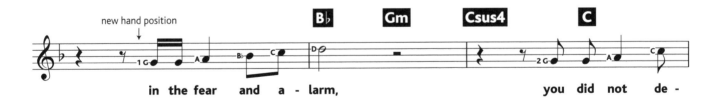

in the fear and a - larm, you did not de-

-sert me, my bro - thers in arms.

Brown Eyed Girl

Words & Music by Van Morrison

Voice: **Soprano saxophone**
Rhythm: **Soft rock**
Tempo: ♩ = 130

Hey, where did we go, days___ when the rains___

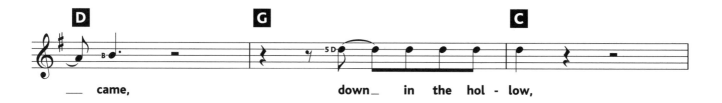

___ came, down___ in the hol - low,

play - ing a new___ game. Laugh - in' and a' run - nin',

skip - pin' and a jump - in' in the mist - y morn -

-ing fog___ with our hearts a' thump-in' and you_

_ my brown eyed girl, ___

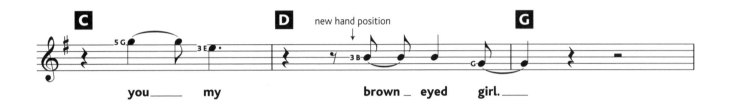

new hand position

you___ my brown_ eyed girl. ___

Do you___ re-mem-ber when we used to sing?_

stretch

_ Sha la__ la la__ la la__ la la__ la la la la la.___

Repeat to fade

Sha la__ la la__ la la__ la la__ la la la la la___

9

Baker Street

Words & Music by Gerry Rafferty

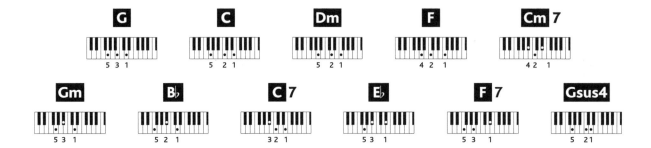

Voice: **Piano**
Rhythm: **Pop ballad**
Tempo: ♩ = 120

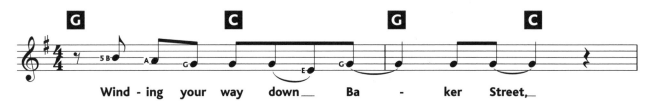

Wind - ing your way down ___ Ba - ker Street, ___

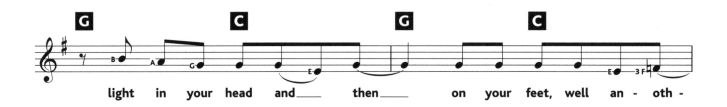

light in your head and ___ then ___ on your feet, well an - oth -

- er cra - zy day, ___ you drink the night ___ a - way, ___ and for -

- get a - bout ev - 'ry - thing. ___

This ci - ty de - sert makes you feel so cold,___ it's got

so ma - ny peo - ple but it's got no soul___ and it's ta -

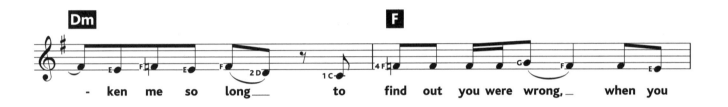

- ken me so long___ to find out you were wrong,___ when you

sort - ed out ev - 'ry - thing.___

You used to think that it was so ea - sy,

you used to say that it was so ea - sy, but

you're try - ing, you're try - ing, now. ___

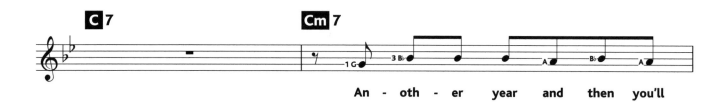

An - oth - er year and then you'll

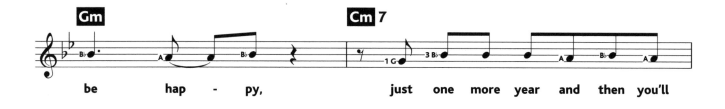

be hap - py, just one more year and then you'll

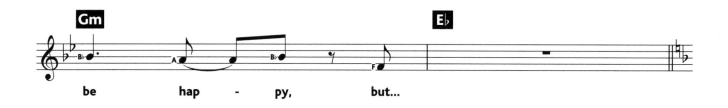

be hap - py, but...

Voice: Saxophone

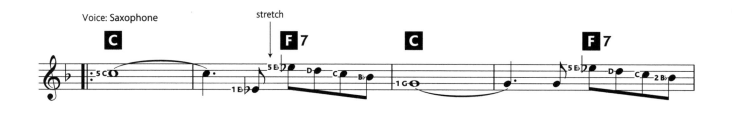

Dancing Queen

Words & Music by Benny Andersson, Stig Anderson & Björn Ulvaeus

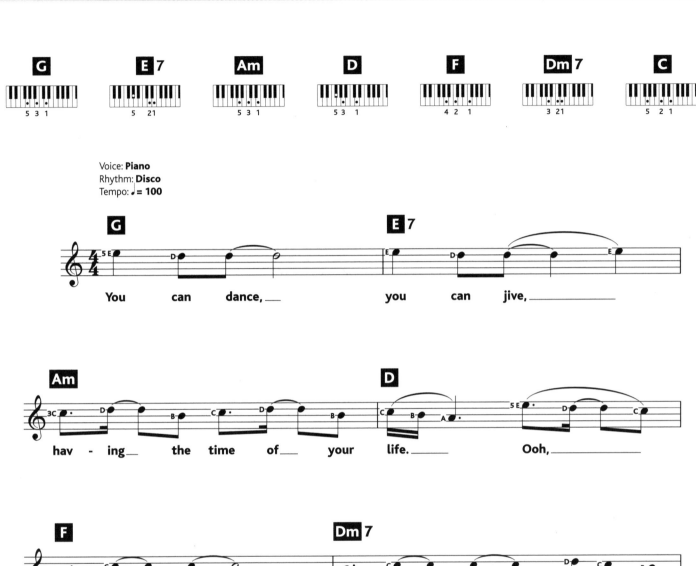

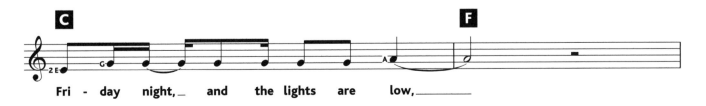

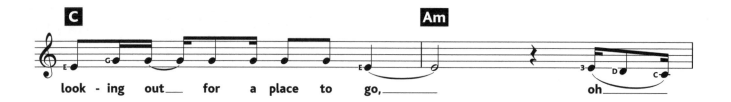

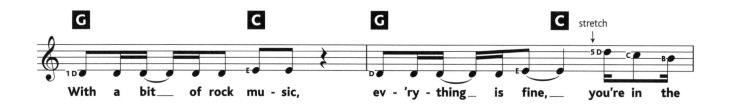

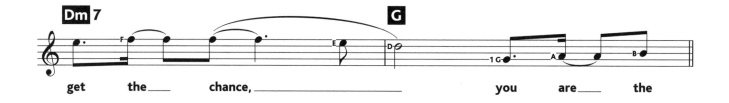

14

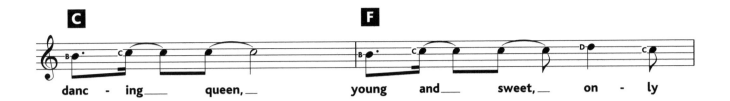

dancing queen, young and sweet, on - ly

se - ven - teen. Dan - cing queen,

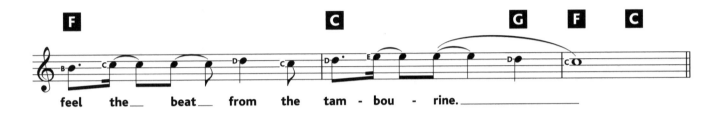

feel the beat from the tam - bou - rine.

You can dance, you can jive,

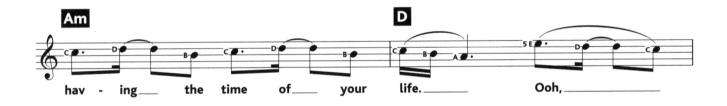

hav - ing the time of your life. Ooh,

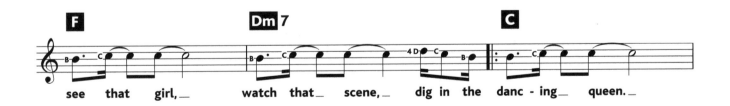

see that girl, watch that scene, dig in the danc - ing queen.

Repeat to fade

Dig in the danc - ing queen. Dig in the

Daydream

Words & Music by John Sebastian

Voice: **Harmonica**
Rhythm: **Swing/Shuffle**
Tempo: ♩ = 98

What a day for a day - dream, what a day for a

day - dream - ing boy. ___ And I'm ___ lost in a day - dream,

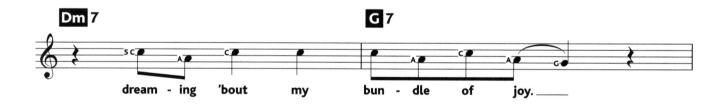

dream - ing 'bout my bun - dle of joy. ___

And ev - en if time ain't real - ly on my side, ___

it's one of those days for tak-ing a walk out-side,___

I'm blow-ing to day to take a walk in the sun,___

and fall on my face on some-bo-dy's new mowed lawn.___

I've been hav-ing a sweet___ dream, I've been dream-ing since I

woke up to-day.___ It's star-ring me and my sweet___ thing,

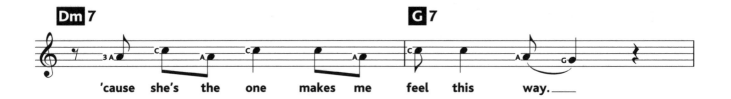

'cause she's the one makes me feel this way.___

And ev - en if time is pass - ing me by a lot,___

I could - n't care less a - bout the dues you say I've got,

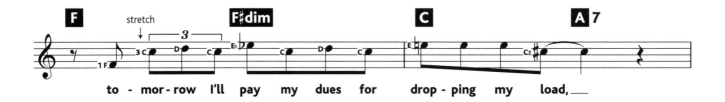

to - mor - row I'll pay my dues for drop - ping my load,___

a pie in the face for be - ing a sleep - y bull toad.___

Don't Let The Sun Go Down On Me

Words & Music by Elton John & Bernie Taupin

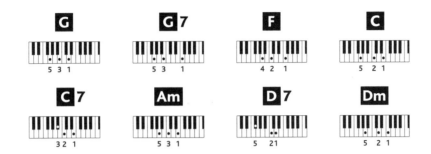

Voice: **Piano**
Rhythm: **8th beat**
Tempo: ♩ = 66

I can't light no more of your dark - - ness.

All my pic - tures _____ seem to fade to black and white.

I'm grow-ing tired, and time stands still be-fore_

me;_ fro - zen here,

19

on the lad - der of my___ life.

Too late___ to save my - self___ from fall - ing,___

I___ took a chance, and changed your way of life.___

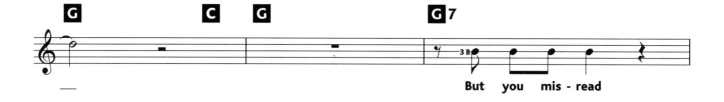

But you mis - read

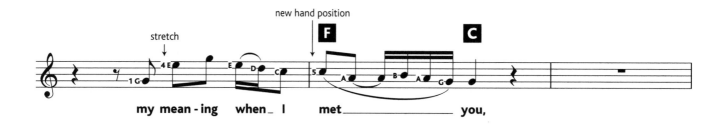

my mean - ing when___ I met___ you,

closed the door and left me blind - ed by___ the light.___

Don't let the sun___ go down on me,

al-though I search my-self, it's al-ways some-one else__ I__ see.___

I'd just al-low a frag-ment of your life___ to wan-der free.___

But los - ing ev - 'ry - thing___ is like the

sun go - ing___ down on___ me. But

los-ing ev - 'ry - thing___ is like the sun go-ing down on___ me.

Englishman In New York

Words & Music by Sting

Voice: **Soprano saxophone**
Rhythm: **Pop rock**
Tempo: ♩ = 96

I don't drink cof - fee, I take tea, my dear.

I like my toast done on one side. You can hear it in my

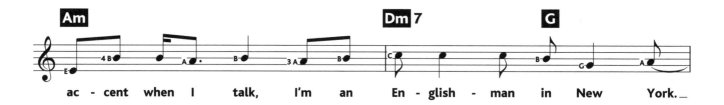

ac - cent when I talk, I'm an En - glish - man in New York.

You see me walk - ing down Fifth A - ve - nue

walk-ing cane here at my side, take it ev-'ry-where I

new hand position

walk, I'm an En-glish-man in New York.___ Woh,___

___ I'm an a-li-en, I'm a le-gal a-li-en, I'm an

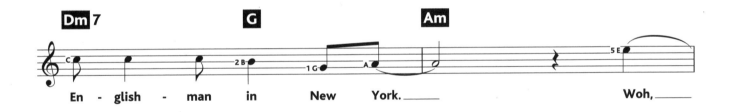

En-glish-man in New York.___ Woh,___

___ I'm an a-li-en, I'm a le-gal a-li-en, I'm an

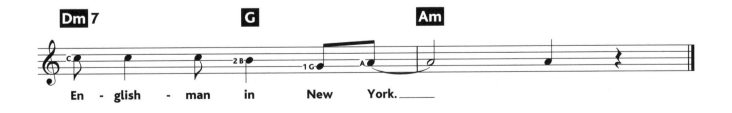

En-glish-man in New York._____

Lean On Me

Words & Music by Bill Withers

Voice: **Piano**
Rhythm: **Soft rock**
Tempo: ♩ = 74

Some - times in our life____ we all have pain,____ we all have sor-

- row.____ But if we are wise____ we know that there's____

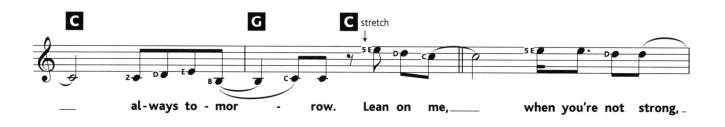

____ al-ways to - mor - row. Lean on me,____ when you're not strong,____

_____ and I'll be your friend,____ I'll help you car - ry__ on.____

For it won't be long_____ till I'm gon-na need__ some-bo-dy to lean_

_____ on.__ Please____ swal-low your pride,_____ if I have things_

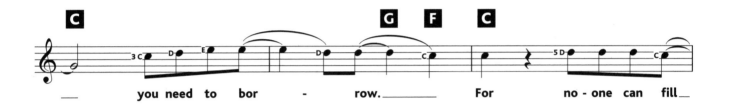

__ you need to bor - row._____ For no - one can fill__

_____ those of your needs__ that you won't let_____ show._

Life On Mars?

Words & Music by David Bowie

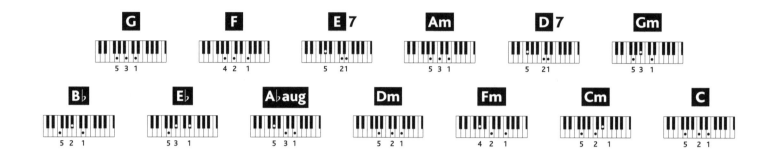

Voice: **Piano**
Rhythm: **Rock ballad**
Tempo: ♩ = 66

It's a God-aw-ful small af-fair   to the girl with the mou-sy hair,

but her mum-my is yell-ing 'no',   and her dad-dy has told_ her to go.

But her friend is no-where to be seen,   now she walks through her sun-ken dream

to the seat with the clear-est view,   and she's hooked to the sil-ver screen.

But the film is a sad-dening bore,   for she's lived it ten times or more,

she could spit in the eyes of fools   as they ask her to fo - cus on

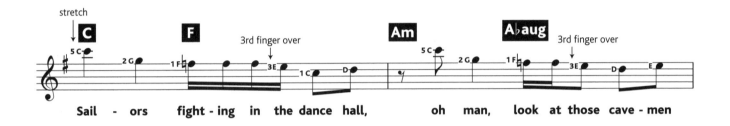

Sail - ors fight - ing in the dance hall,   oh man, look at those cave - men

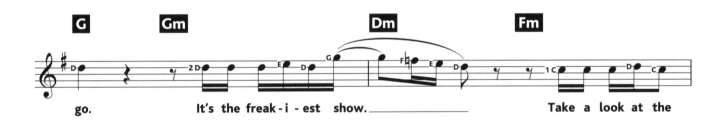

go.   It's the freak-i-est show._____   Take a look at the

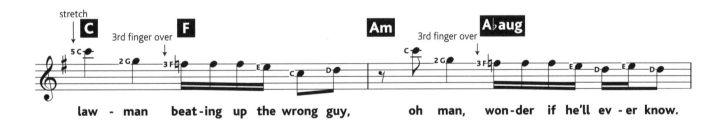

law - man beat-ing up the wrong guy,   oh man, won-der if he'll ev - er know.

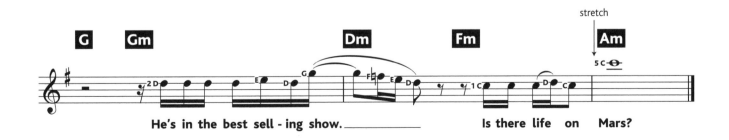

He's in the best sell - ing show._____   Is there life on Mars?

Light My Fire

Words & Music by Jim Morrison, Robbie Krieger, Ray Manzarek & John Densmore

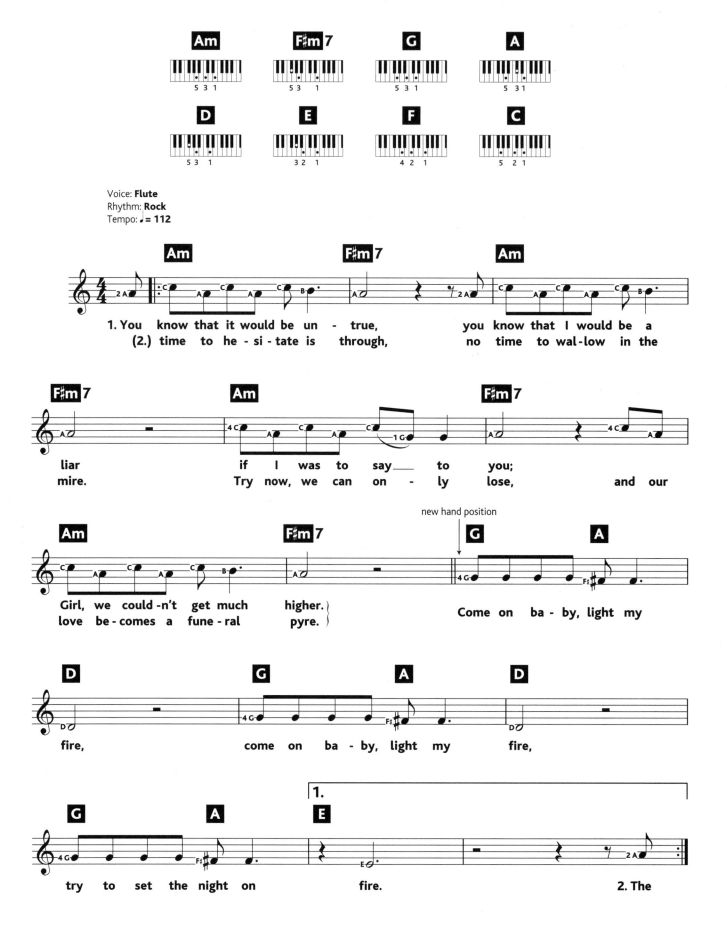

3. The time to he-si-tate is through, no

time to wal-low in the mire. Try now, we can on - ly

lose, and our love be-comes a fune - ral pyre.

new hand position

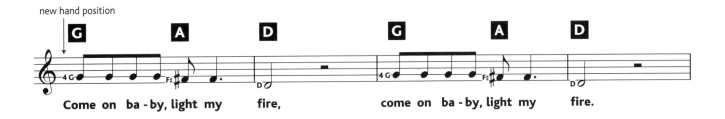

Come on ba - by, light my fire, come on ba - by, light my fire.

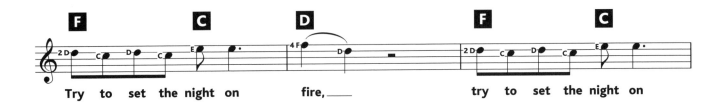

Try to set the night on fire,_____ try to set the night on

fire._____ Try to set the night on fire._____

The Long And Winding Road

Words & Music by John Lennon & Paul McCartney

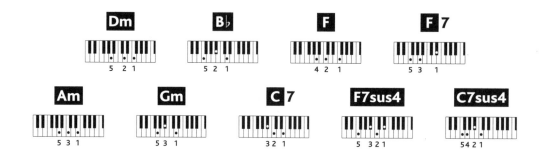

Voice: **Oboe**
Rhythm: **Soft rock**
Tempo: ♩ = 78

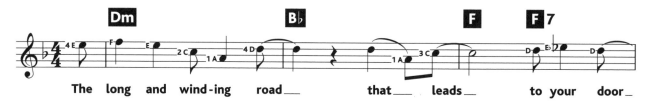

The long and wind-ing road ___ that ___ leads ___ to your door ___

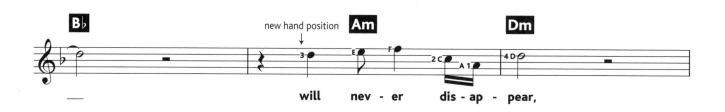

___ will nev - er dis - ap - pear,

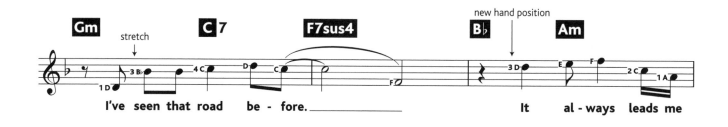

I've seen that road be - fore. _____ It al - ways leads me

here, leads me to your door. ___

Ma - ny times__ I've been a - lone and ma - ny times__ I've cried.__

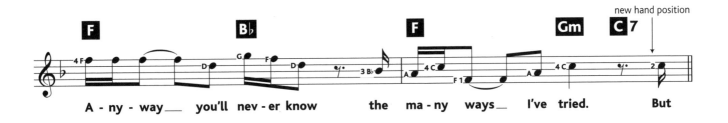

A - ny - way__ you'll nev - er know the ma - ny ways__ I've tried. But

still they lead me back___ to the long___ wind - ing road.__

___ You left me stand - ing here

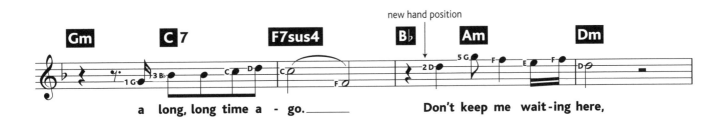

a long, long time a - go._____ Don't keep me wait - ing here,

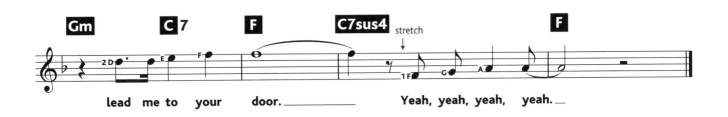

lead me to your door._____ Yeah, yeah, yeah, yeah.___

Maggie May

Words & Music by Rod Stewart & Martin Quittenton

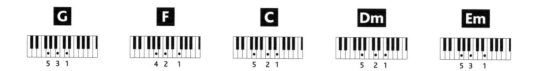

Voice: **Organ**
Rhythm: **Rock**
Tempo: ♩ = 122

Wake up Mag-gie I think I got some-thing to say to you.

It's late Sep-tem-ber and I real-ly should be

back at school. I know I keep you a-mused,

but I feel I'm be-ing used. Oh

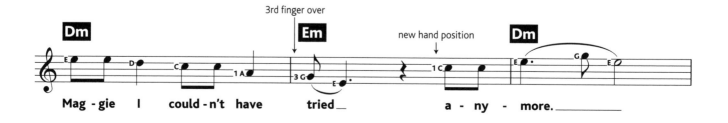

Mag-gie I could-n't have tried a-ny-more.

You lured me a-way from home, just to

save you from be-ing a - lone. You stole my heart and that's

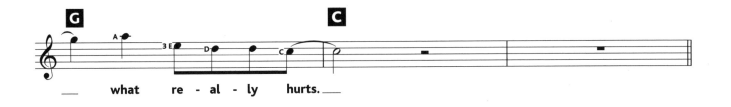

what re - al - ly hurts.

Waterloo Sunset

Words & Music by Ray Davies

Voice: **Piano**
Rhythm: **Soft rock**
Tempo: ♩ = 106

Dir - ty old ri - ver must you keep roll - ing, flow-ing in-to

__ the night? __ Peo - ple so bu - sy, make me feel diz-

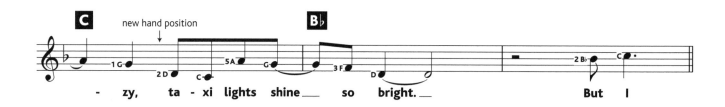

- zy, ta - xi lights shine __ so bright. __ But I

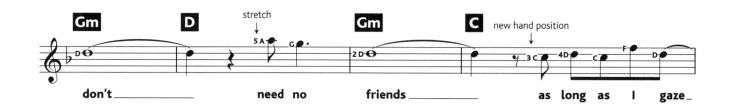

don't __ need no friends __ as long as I gaze __

on Wa-ter-loo Sun - set, I am in pa - ra - dise.

Ev -'ry day I look at the world from my win - dow.

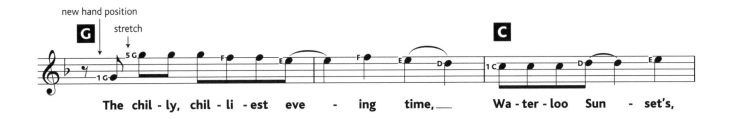

The chil - ly, chil - li -est eve - ing time, Wa - ter - loo Sun - set's,

Wa - ter - loo Sun - set's fine.

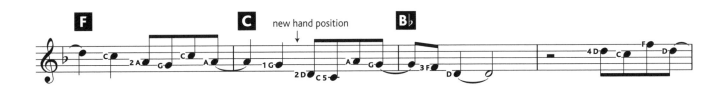

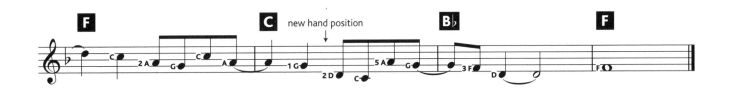

Wild World

Words & Music by Cat Stevens

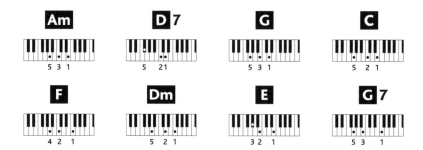

Voice: **Acoustic guitar**
Rhythm: **8th beat**
Tempo: ♩ = **72**

La la la la la la la la la la___ la la la la la la la la la__

___ la la la la la la la la la la la.

Now that I've lost ev-'ry-thing to you,___ you say you wan-na start some-thing new,__

___ and it's break-ing my heart, you're leav-ing. Ba-by I'm griev-ing.

But if you want to leave take good care, hope you have a lot of nice things to wear, __

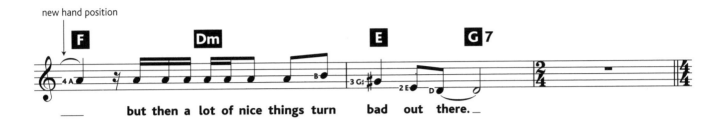

__ but then a lot of nice things turn bad out there. __

Oh, ba - by, ba - by it's a wild world.

It's hard to get by, just up - on a smile.

Oh, ba - by, ba - by it's a wild world.

I'll al - ways re - mem - ber you __ like a child, girl. __

Woman

Words & Music by John Lennon

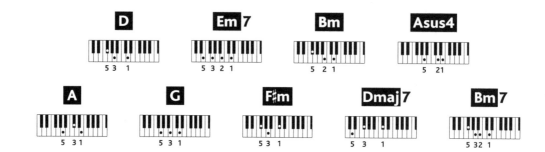

Voice: **Flute**
Rhythm: **Soft rock**
Tempo: ♩ = 85

Wo - man,   I   can   hard - ly   ex - press,

my   mixed   e - mo - tions   at   my   thought -less - ness, ___

af - ter   all,   I'm   for - ev - er   in   your   debt, ___   and

wo - man   I   will   try   to   ex - press,

my in - ner feel - ings and thank - ful ness. ___

for show - ing me the mean - ing of suc -

- cess. ___

Ooh, ___ well, well, doo, doo, doo,

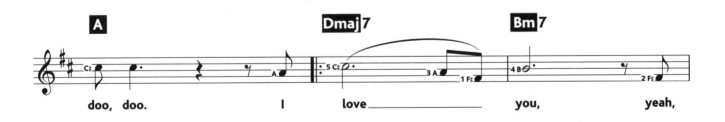

doo, doo. I love ___ you, yeah,

yeah, now and for - ev - er. I

Bringing you the words and the music

All the latest music in print... rock & pop plus jazz, blues, country, classical and the best in West End show scores.

- Books to match your favourite CDs.

- Book-and-CD titles with high quality backing tracks for you to play along to. Now you can play guitar or piano with your favourite artist... or simply sing along!

- Audition songbooks with CD backing tracks for both male and female singers for all those with stars in their eyes.

- Can't read music? No problem, you can still play all the hits with our wide range of chord songbooks.

- Check out our range of instrumental tutorial titles, taking you from novice to expert in no time at all!

- Musical show scores include *The Phantom Of The Opera*, *Les Misérables*, *Mamma Mia* and many more hit productions.

- DVD master classes featuring the techniques of top artists.